D0358633

CONTENTS

POWERED BY KINDNESS · BORN TO LEAD · STAND STRONG

POSITIVE ATTITUDE CHANGES EVERYTHING (PACE)!

Hi there!

Come and dive into my world and find out all about me, my family and my amazing friends. You'll find stories, puzzles, activities and quizzes inside this fun Annual, as well as opportunities to find out more about yourself. Always show your sparkle!

Barbie x

How many times can you find the word **DREAMS** in this Annual?

....

I have three sisters and live in Malibu, California. I moved to Malibu from Wisconsin when I was 8 years old. My parents wanted us to live near the beach, which is lucky because I love surfing! I spend time sharing new ideas about things such as music, films and personal style. I'm also super curious about so many things, which means I like to ask questions and talk. Like, 'what if'? What if... I was an inventor? Or what if... I was a magical mermaid?! What's super important to me is spending time with my sisters and friends and sharing ideas with them. I think it's important to be who you want to be.

Check out these selfie close-ups! Draw a line to what they are of.

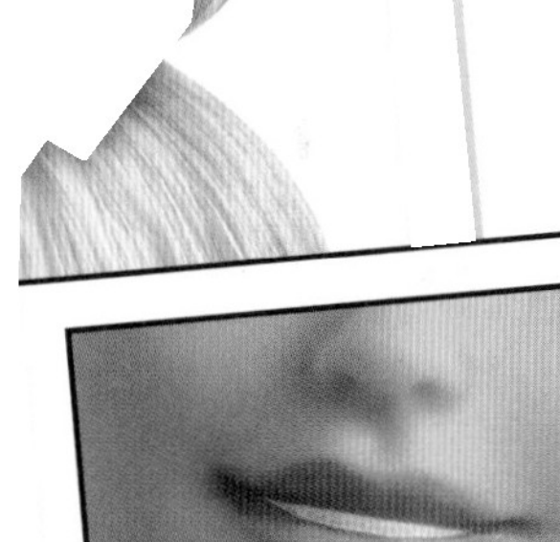

My spirit animal is...

A HORSE

I TOTALLY LOVE...

- Animals
- Expressing myself
- Playing the piano
- Going to the beach
- Vlogging
- My friends
- Singing

My motto is...

Do it Anyway!

I WOULD INVENT... A TELEPORTATION DEVICE!

My best qualities are...

I'm CURIOUS and IMAGINATIVE

I'M AFRAID OF... FORGETTING HOW GRATEFUL I AM

(and spiders!)

MY FAVOURITE SCHOOL CLASSES ARE...

English & Science

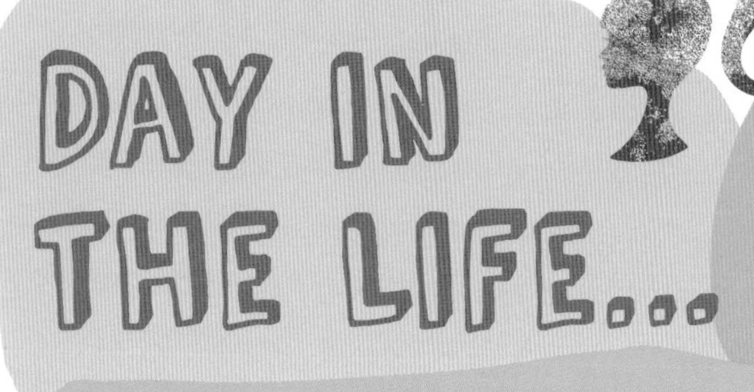

Hang out with Barbie and find out about her day by spotting these 10 words in the wordsearch below.

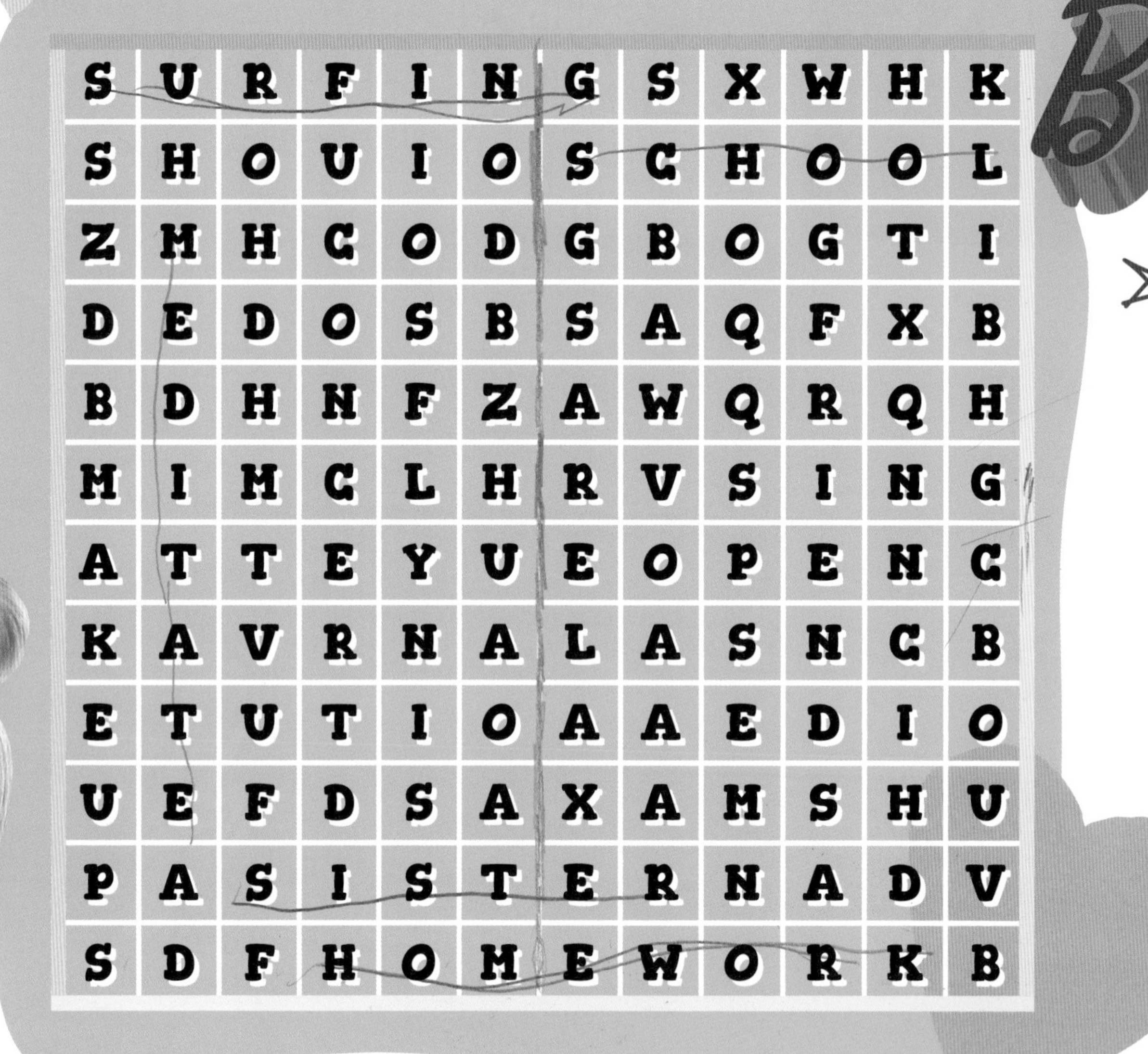

MEDITATE
SISTER
SURFING
SCHOOL
HOMEWORK
RELAX
SING
MAKEUP
FRIENDS
CONCERT

Answers on pages 76-77

GIRL POWER

Be who you want to be and design your very own logo on the back of this jacket. Use colouring pencils or paint to add colour.

RISE AND SHINE

BRAVE BOLD

FEAR LESS

LIVING THE DREAM

Barbie likes nothing better than hanging out in her Dreamhouse bedroom. Can you find 10 differences between these two pictures?

COLOUR IN A HEART FOR EACH DIFFERENCE YOU SPOT

Answers on pages 76-77

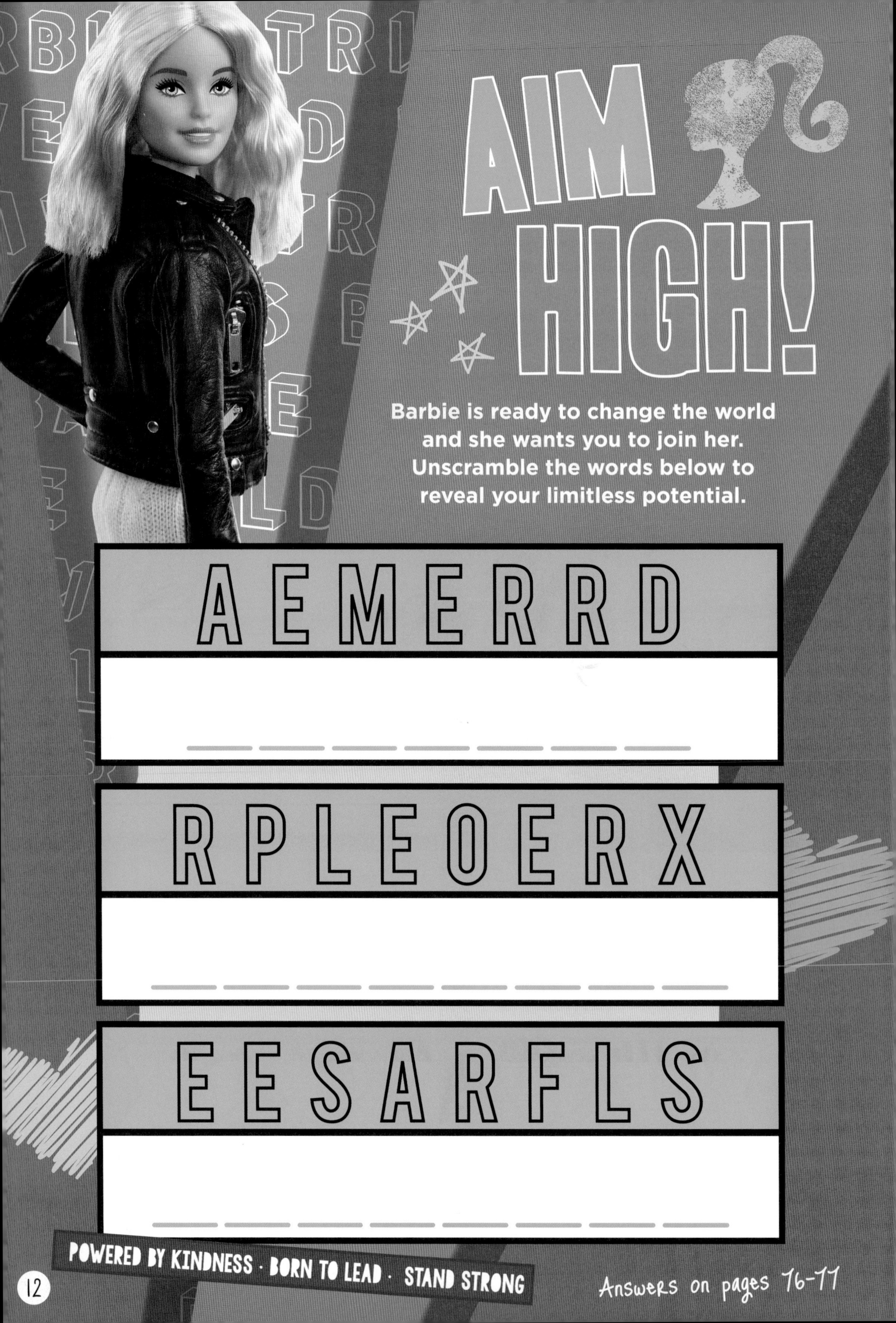

AIM HIGH!

Barbie is ready to change the world and she wants you to join her. Unscramble the words below to reveal your limitless potential.

AEMERRD

_ _ _ _ _ _ _

RPLEOERX

_ _ _ _ _ _ _ _

EESARFLS

_ _ _ _ _ _ _ _

POWERED BY KINDNESS · BORN TO LEAD · STAND STRONG

Answers on pages 76-77

KINDNESS IS KEY

Barbie's friends believe that we rise by lifting others. Help spread kindness by writing down five kind things to do.

#01

#02

#03

#04

#05

Barbie and her band are ready to take to the stage, but they need another band member. Create your very own water xylophone instrument so you can make music and be the star of the show.

YOU WILL NEED

- A large jug of water
- Drinking glasses x 6
- Food colouring
- A wooden spoon

STEP 1

Fill the jug with water and pour the water into the glasses. Fill them up to different levels, from fullest to emptiest glass.

Using the food colouring and following the instructions on the packet, add to the water in each glass to create six different colours.

STEP 3

Use a wooden spoon to tap each glass and listen to the different notes each glass makes. Now you're ready to create your own music!

Strike a POSE

A few of these selfies are a bit too close up. Which one belongs to the picture of Barbie and her friend, who are ready to go to a party?

Check out these super cool nail designs that Barbie is trying to choose from at the salon. Colour them in and then add your own daring designs to Barbie's nails.

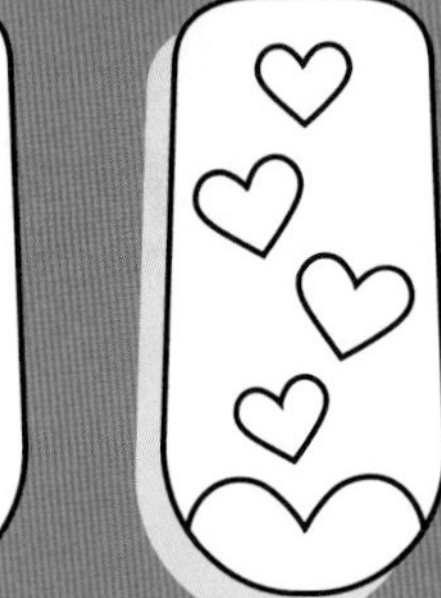

Barbie

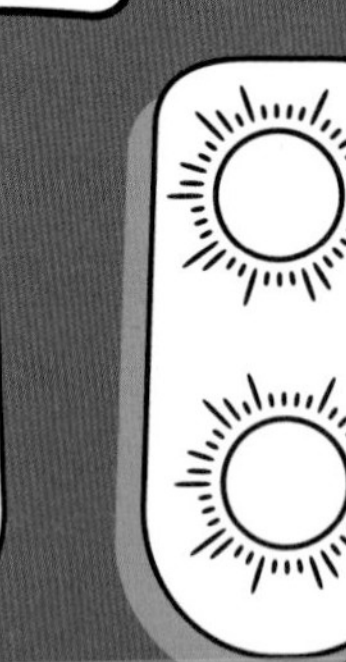

SUNNY DAYS

There's nothing better than spending time outdoors in the park with your friends. Find the missing pieces of this picture and draw a line to where they belong.

Answers on pages 76-77

SISTERS Shine
TOGETHER

Unscramble the letters in these words to reveal each sisters' name.

SCEAELH ___ ___ ___ ___ ___ ___ ___

ISPRKPE ___ ___ ___ ___ ___ ___ ___

ISCEAT ___ ___ ___ ___ ___ ___

Stacie

Stacie is fearless. Like, she'll do anything and face her fears to get what she wants. And, boy, does she know what she wants. She is so much fun to be around; we always have a laugh when we're together. Stacie is also completely ace at sports and really competitive. But the best thing about her is that she is so brave. I would love to have her courage.

CHELSEA

Meet my littlest sister, who is 6 years old. **She wants to know EVERYTHING!** She asks a lot of questions and she's also super smart. But my favourite thing about her is her silliness. She loves playing pranks, a good tickle fight and skipping. She'd skip everywhere if she could.

SISTER GOALS

Ever wondered which sister you're most like? Well, now you can find out by taking this quiz!

1 YOU HAVE A BIT OF SPARE TIME ON YOUR HANDS. WOULD YOU:

a) Cook up a super fun prank to play on the next person you see?

b) Chill out and listen to the latest track from your favourite band?

c) Find a friend to play football with and practise taking penalties?

2 IT'S TIME TO CHOOSE AN OUTFIT FROM YOUR WARDROBE. DO YOU CHOOSE:

a) A super-cute unicorn t-shirt and pink skirt?

b) Your favourite comfy jeans and shirt?

c) Football shorts, a sports top and hoody?

3 BARBIE WOULD LOVE TO SEE WHAT'S IN YOUR BAG. WILL SHE FIND:

a) A super-cuddly stuffed toy?

b) Headphones?

c) A football?

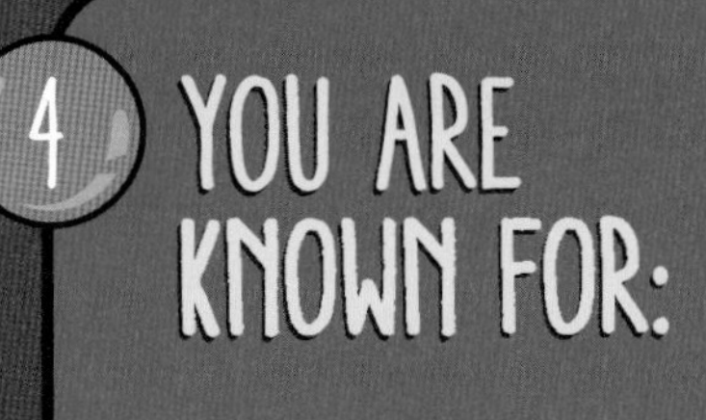

4 YOU ARE KNOWN FOR:

a) Throwing the BEST tea party around.

b) Being totally tech savvy.

c) Loving a challenge and being very competitive.

5 WHAT WORD WOULD YOUR FRIENDS USE TO DESCRIBE YOU:

a) Imaginative?

b) Independent?

c) Fearless?

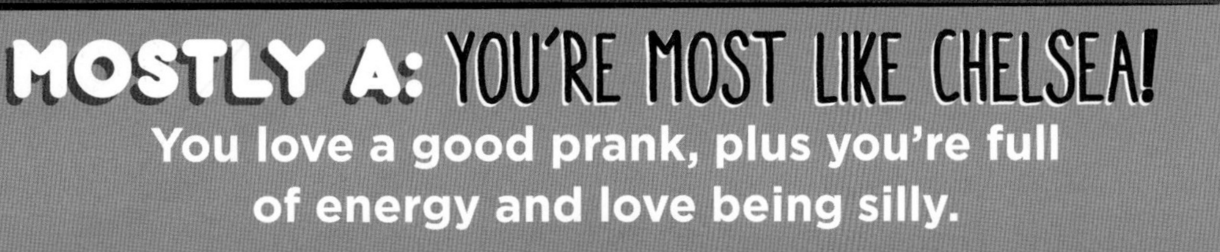

MOSTLY A: YOU'RE MOST LIKE CHELSEA!

You love a good prank, plus you're full of energy and love being silly.

MOSTLY B: YOU'RE MOST LIKE SKIPPER!

Just like Barbie's biggest little sister, you're calm, confident and really into your music.

MOSTLY C: YOU'RE MOST LIKE STACIE!

You're a champ at sports, full of optimism and always up for trying something new.

LET'S ROCK!

Barbie and her band need to get to the concert pronto to make sure they make it on stage on time. Find a way through this maze to help them be able to shine on stage.

START

Barbie AND ROCKERS

Answers on pages 76-77

FINISH
Barbie
ROCKERS

YOU CAN BE A DOCTOR

One morning, Barbie arrived at the children's clinic where she was spending the day volunteering. Her favourite nurse, Mira, asked Barbie to sit in the waiting room until she was ready for Barbie to get started.

As she sat in the waiting room, she noticed that there were children with runny noses and earaches. Barbie thought about how she could help them – and the doctor!

Barbie sat next to a girl with a purple cast on her arm. It was covered in doodles.

"I like your cast," Barbie said to the girl.

"Thanks, but it's coming off today," said the girl with a worried look. "And I'm scared it will hurt."

Barbie knew how she felt; she used to be scared to go to the doctor's, too. So, Barbie told the girl about her friend Nikki, who said it tickled when they took her cast off.

Just then, nurse Mira called Barbie's name.

"It was nice to meet you," said Barbie. "And don't worry, Dr Vargas is the nicest doctor you'll ever meet. When you're finished, she has a secret treasure box for you to pick a treat from."

Nurse Mira smiled at Barbie. "It looks like you already have a good bedside manner," she said.

Mira introduced Barbie to the first patient. "Oliver is here for his well-visit," said the nurse, handing Barbie Oliver's chart. "It's a check-up to make sure he is healthy and growing."

Barbie bent down and introduced herself. Oliver was bouncing on the table.

Nurse Mira and Barbie weighed Oliver and then measured how tall he was.

"Wow, you look very tall today, Oliver," Mira said to him. Oliver giggled to himself and Barbie noticed he was standing on his tiptoes.

"Let's try with your feet flat on the floor now," Mira said as Barbie made a note of his real height.

Next, nurse Mira checked Oliver's blood pressure. "This is so we know that your heart is strong," she told him.

Then the nurse checked his eyesight. After every check, Barbie wrote the information in Oliver's chart. It was important to make sure it was all correct as the doctor would use it to make sure that Oliver was healthy and well.

While Barbie was writing, Dr Vargas knocked and entered the room. "Wow Oliver, you have grown so tall," she said when she saw who her patient was. The doctor then continued with the rest of the exam.

She checked his ears with an otoscope and then listened to his lungs with a stethoscope.

Dr Vargas asked Oliver questions about his friends and how well he sleeps at night. "There's more to being healthy than blood pressure and height," Dr Vargas told Barbie.

The doctor looked over Barbie's notes on Oliver's chart. "Everything looks great, Oliver. You're healthy, happy, and ready to start school!"

The clinic was busy that day and there was already another patient waiting.

After washing their hands, the doctor checked the patient's chart that was hanging on the door and smiled at Barbie.

"Nurse Mira mentioned that you have a great bedside manner, so I think you'll be a lot of help during this next exam," she said to Barbie.

When Barbie entered the exam room, she saw a familiar face.

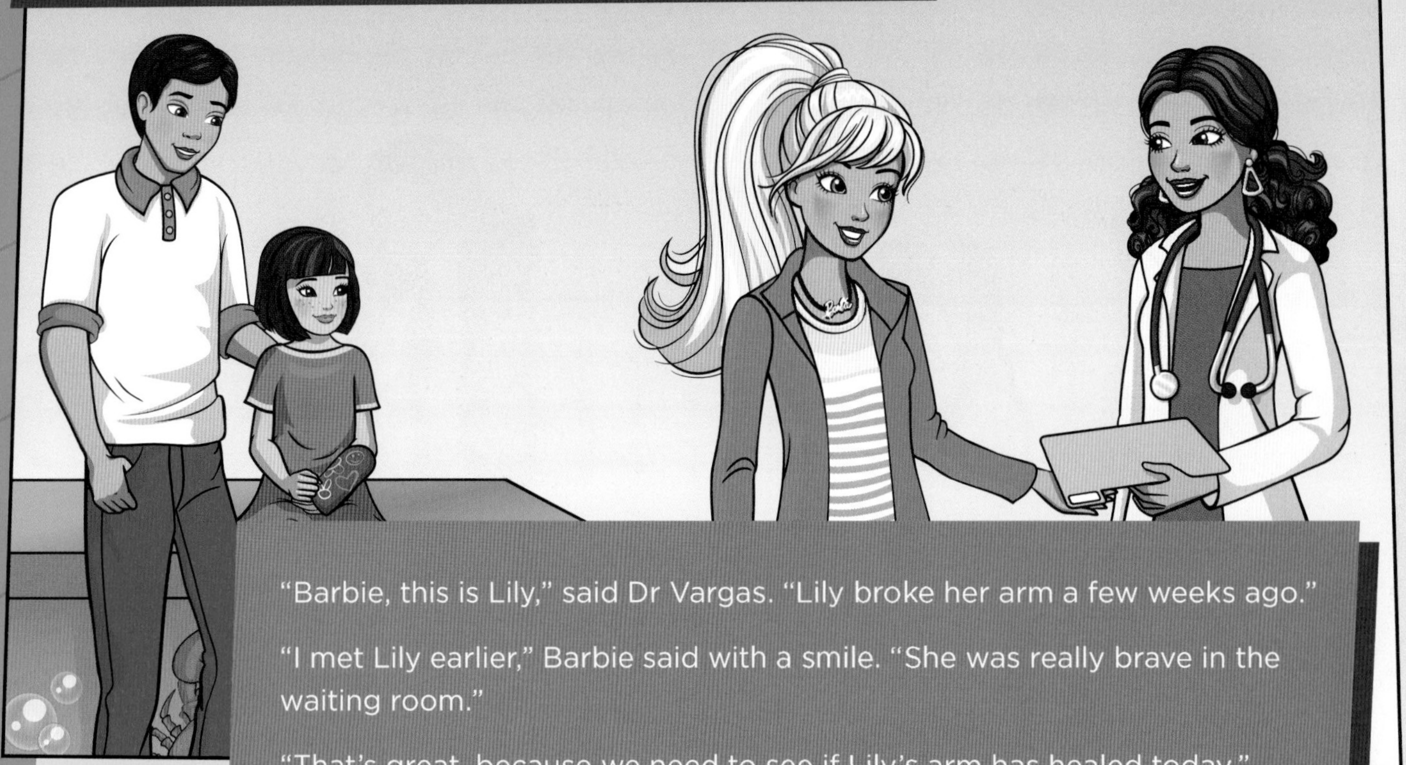

"Barbie, this is Lily," said Dr Vargas. "Lily broke her arm a few weeks ago."

"I met Lily earlier," Barbie said with a smile. "She was really brave in the waiting room."

"That's great, because we need to see if Lily's arm has healed today," said Dr Vargas. "Can you take her to the x-ray machine next door?"

A friendly x-ray technician welcomed them into the room. As an x-ray technician, she set up a machine to take pictures of Lily's bones inside her body.

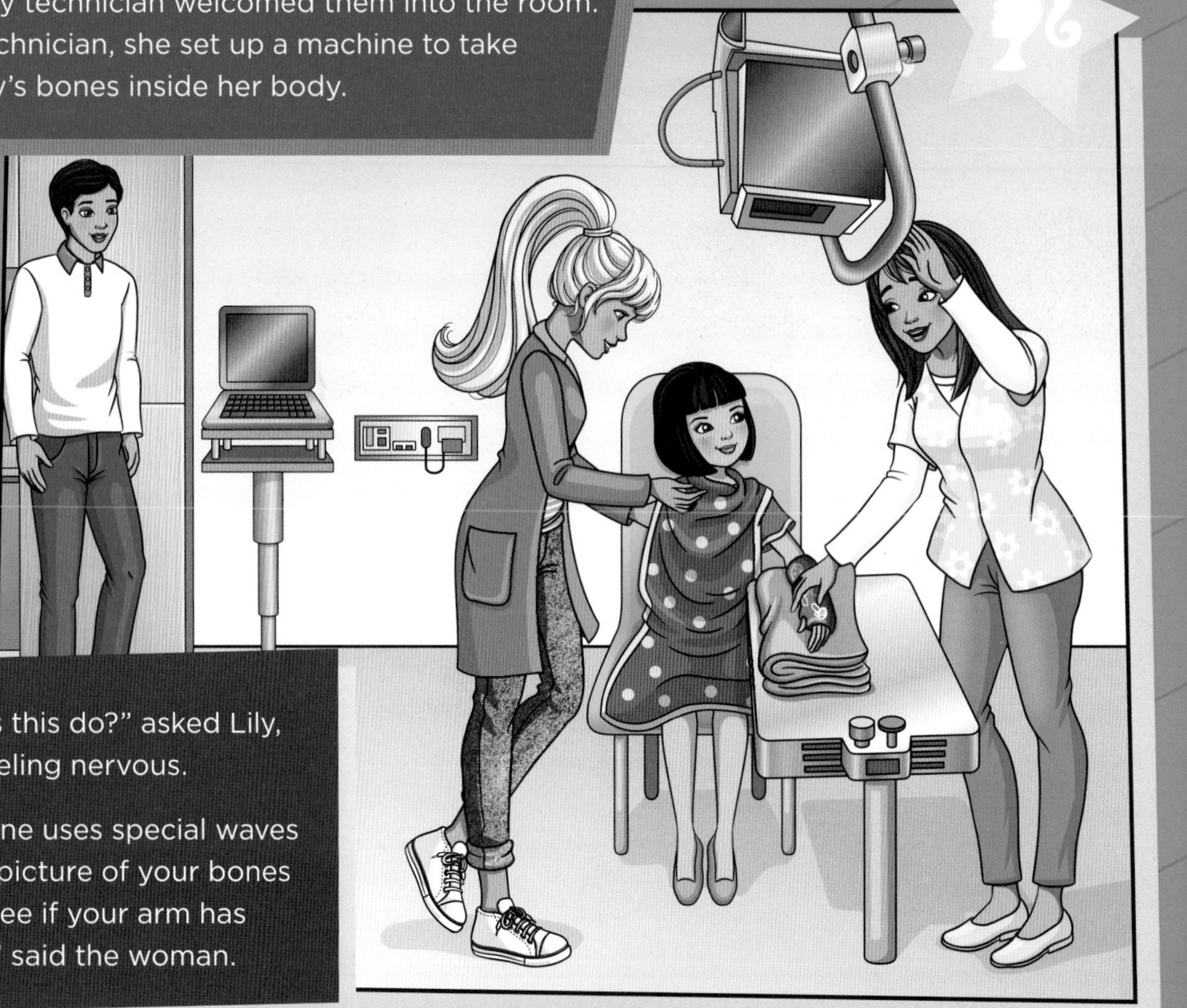

"What does this do?" asked Lily, who was feeling nervous.

"This machine uses special waves to create a picture of your bones so we can see if your arm has healed yet," said the woman.

When the x-ray pictures were ready, Dr Vargas took a close look at them. "This is the first x-ray of your broken arm," she said, pointing to the first picture. "And this is the x-ray we just took."

Barbie could see that the broken bone was completely healed.

"It looks like your cast will be coming off today," said the doctor with a smile.

First, Dr Vargas used a special cast saw that vibrated and cut the cast.

"It does tickle!" Lily laughed, even though the cast saw made a very loud and scary noise.

Next, Dr Vargas used a cast spreader to separate the cast.

Then she let Barbie cut the padding, which was underneath the cast, with a pair of scissors.

"All done!" announced Dr Vargas. Lily bent her fingers and waved her hand. She was so pleased that it had healed and the cast could come off.

"Can I keep the cast?" Lily asked, excitedly.

"Of course!" said Dr Vargas.

"And can you and Barbie sign it, too?" smiled Lily.

"I would love to," said Barbie as she wrote her name on the purple cast.

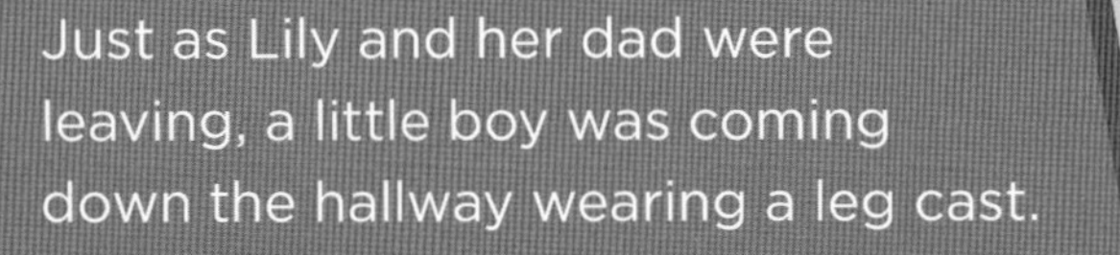

"Don't worry, it's not scary. And Barbie and Dr Vargas are the nicest!" Lily told him. "And, best of all, there's a secret treasure box."

"Are you ready for our next patient, Barbie?" asked Dr Vargas.

"Of course!" said Barbie. She couldn't wait to see who they were going to help next!

LET'S WRITE A STORY!

Take turns with a friend, each writing a sentence of a story.

Barbie

Build on the previous sentence to make the story flow.

You could write a 'You Can Be...' story, just like the one you've just read.

Don't forget to use describing words.

Now, it's time to create a super cool cover for your story. Create a design for your book cover and then colour it in.

Do you want to draw a character or a scene?

Think about the title of the story. Can you add it?

DREAM BIG

Know no limits because you can be a... scientist! Take a look at these science labs – which is the odd one out?

A

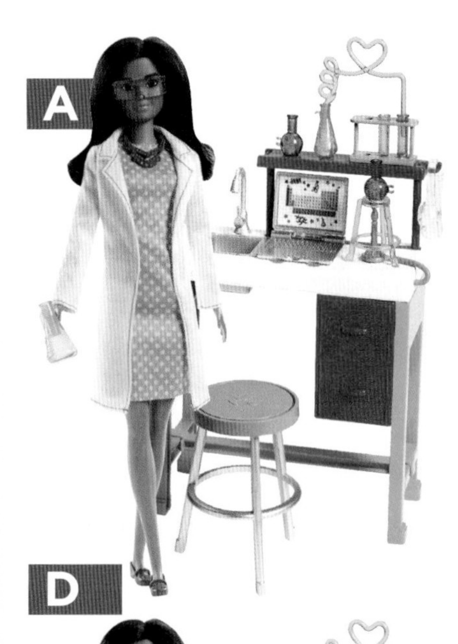

B

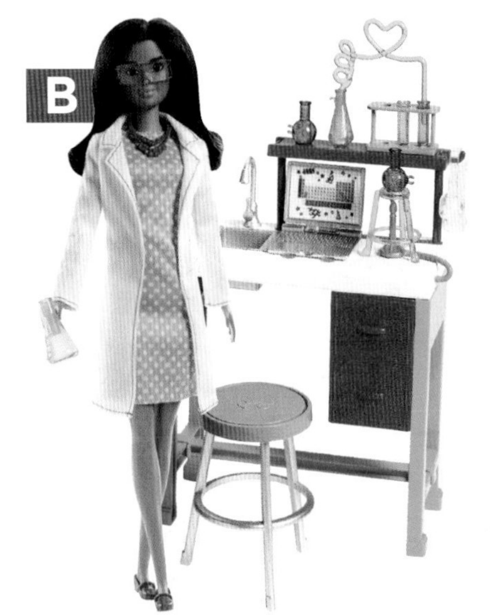

C

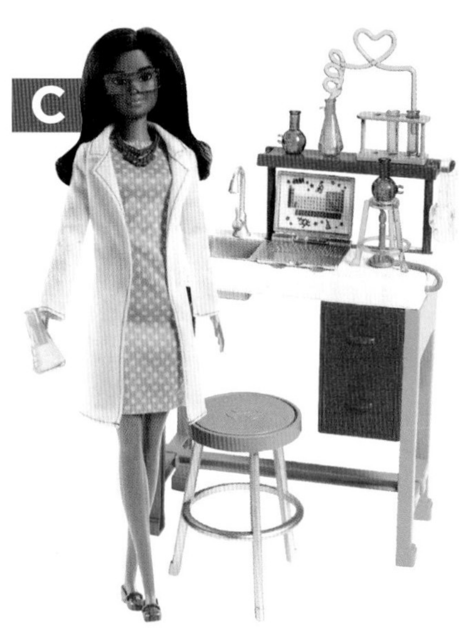

D

E

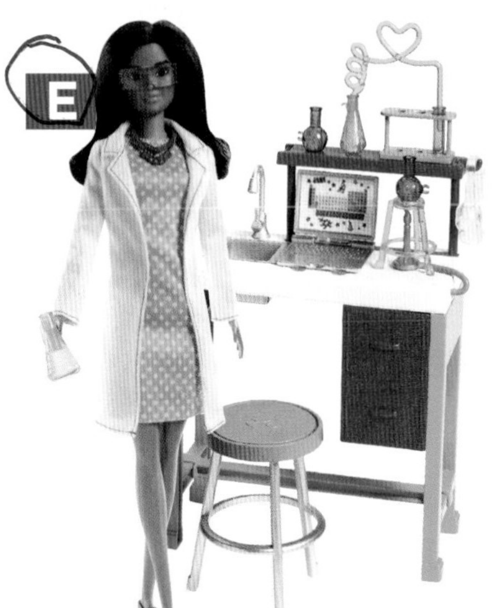

F

Answers on pages 76-77

MATCH IT
Barbie's wardrobe is bursting with fun and inspiring outfits and accessories. Match each one to the job or hobby that she needs them for.
SKATEBOARDER
PILOT
CONSTRUCTION WORKER
NURSE
FOOTBALL PLAYER
ICE SKATER
MUSICIAN
VET
Answers on pages 76-77

All Mixed Up

Put the scenes from You Can Be A Doctor story in the correct order by numbering them 1 to 8.

Answers on pages 76-77

PET PROFILES

How many animal friends have you met on these pages? Write your answer here

DJ

- Boy pup
- Belongs to Skipper
- Moves to the beat of his own tail
- Wears a silver-studded black collar
- Loves dancing to music
- Likes headphones and sunglasses
- Would say "My howl is the next big thing."

Honey

- Girl pup
- Belongs to Chelsea
- Sweet, curious and optimistic
- Wears a purple collar with flowers
- Loves chasing her tail
- Likes dressing up
- Would say "I got it right, yay me!"

Rookie

- Boy pup
- Belongs to Stacie
- Always has a plan!
- Wears a blue bandana
- Loves running, jumping, flips and pouncing
- Likes frisbees, balls, ropes – anything to play with
- Would say "I bet I can dig the fastest."

Taffy

- Girl pup
- Belongs to Barbie
- Shy but wants to be brave
- Wears a diamond-studded pink collar
- Loves cuddling or nuzzling
- Likes a blanket or small cuddly toy
- Would say "I'm not a scaredy dog!"

Blissa

- Girl cat
- Always purrs for Barbie
- Doesn't always know what she wants
- Wears a pink collar (and sometimes a bow)
- Loves napping, eating and pampering
- Likes her toy Mew Mew
- Doesn't like water, balls of wool, bugs or climbing trees.

Misty

- Girl horse
- Beautiful and expressive
- Always ready to offer Barbie a ride
- Met Barbie when she worked at the Stables
- Wears a pink rein and saddle
- Loves dancing.

PUPPY LOVE

There's a whole lotta love for the Roberts' pets. Join the dots to reveal the pet that Barbie is hanging out with, then colour in the picture!

FUR-BULOUS FRIENDS

The cute little pups have lost each other. Help them through the maze so they can be together again.

Answers on pages 76-77

GOT THE MESSAGE?

Barbie has just sent a secret text message to Nikki. Can you break the code to reveal what it says?

Answers on pages 76-77

Seek & Shine

Keep those eyes peeled and see if you can find Barbie wearing her favourite shades.

Answers on pages 76-77

PET PALS

Barbie and her sisters love taking care of their pets. Draw a line to match each pet to its shadow.

DREAM PATTERNS

Join the Dreamhouse Adventures by completing the patterns below. Draw or write the name of each missing picture.

CITY DREAMS

Barbie and her friends are living the dream in the city. Put this picture of them in the correct order.

A

B

C

D

E

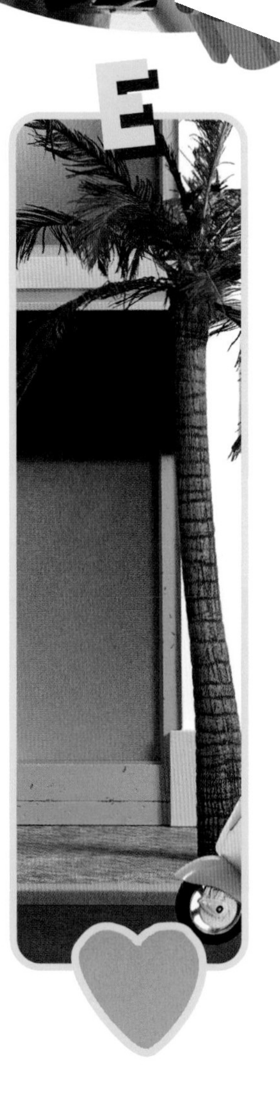

ANSWER:

Answers on pages 76-77

ONE OF A KIND

It's time to celebrate you! Write down things that you like about yourself here.

FRECKLE

LOUD

AP IN EETH

WEAR GLASSES

SHY

CURLY HAIR

BIG FEET

Holiday Treats

Christmas is just around the corner and Barbie and her friends have been baking up a storm in the kitchen. Can you spot all the objects in this sweet scene?

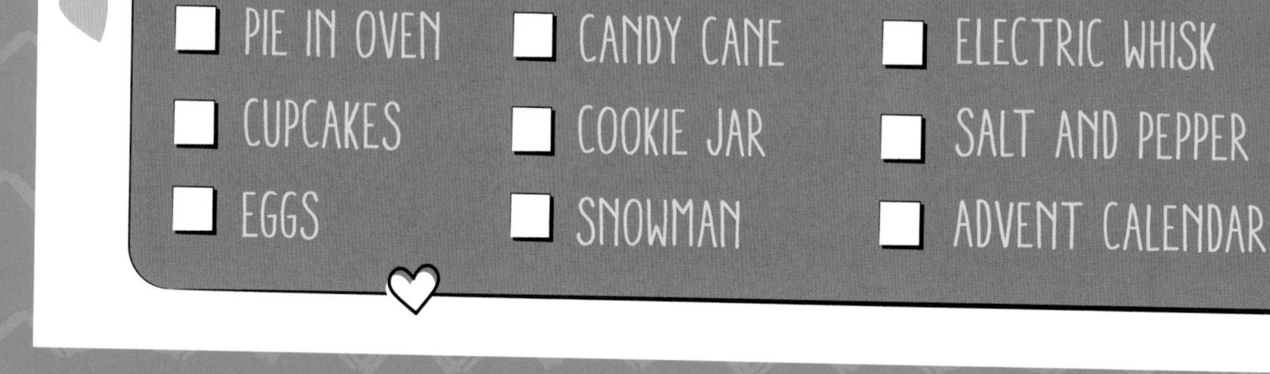

KICK IT

Barbie's cool collection of trainers and boots are bursting out of her wardrobe. Match all the shoes by drawing a line between them.

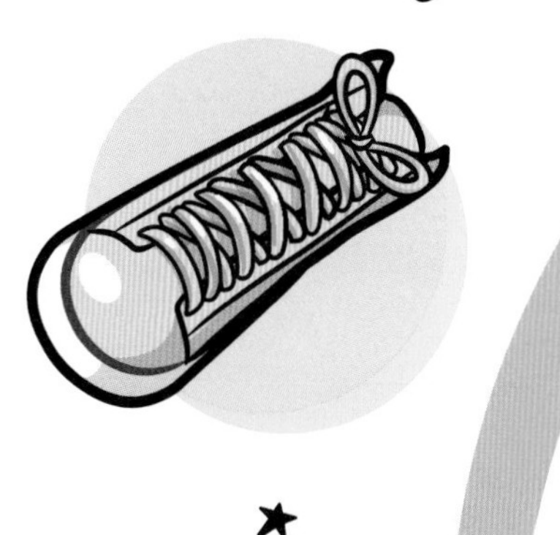

ROAD TRIP!

It was a beautiful, sunny Malibu morning. Barbie and her friends were hanging out at the pool, having loads of fun. Daisy was playing a record on her turntable and Barbie's sisters were dancing to the beat.

Suddenly, the record let out a loud SCRAATCCHHH and the music stopped.

"I don't believe it!" Daisy cried out. She was looking at a text message she had just received.

"A DJ has sprained his wrist and he wants me to replace him at the huge music festival in the desert."

"With, like, thousands and thousands and thousands of people?" Renee chimed in.

"Daisy, this is awesome!" Barbie said. "It's your dream!"

Daisy smiled back. "I know," she replied. "Yay!"

But all she could think about was Renee's "thousands of people" comment.

"Music festival in the desert? You know what that means, right?" Nikki asked her friends.

The girls exchanged excited smiles. "ROAD TRIP!" they cheered.

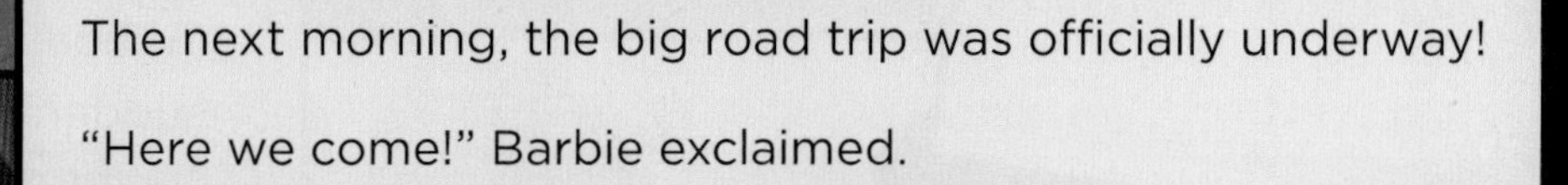

The next morning, the big road trip was officially underway!

"Here we come!" Barbie exclaimed.

They were only a few miles from home when Teresa suddenly cried out, "Barbie, STOP!" Barbie hit the brakes.

"Daisy!" Teresa asked in alarm, "Where's your turntable?"

Daisy thought that maybe she'd left her turntable back at Barbie's house. So, Barbie turned the camper around and drove home. Daisy couldn't exactly DJ at the festival without it!

Skipper was waiting in the driveway with Daisy's turntable. "Here you go!" Skipper said, handing it to Daisy. "I found it in the freezer!"

"Sorry, guys," Daisy said when they were back on the road again. "I must have left it in there when I was, um . . . uh . . . getting some ice," she added.

"I just can't stop thinking about the concert tonight!" she went on. "My head's all full of, like, what songs should I play? And what should I end with? And—"

"Whoa! Check it out!" Nikki said suddenly, looking at her phone. "According to this, there's going to be the biggest crowd ever at the festival.

Daisy tried to laugh along with her friends, but she felt butterflies in her stomach.

A few moments later, something on the highway caught her eye.

"Stop!" she cried.

"It's Dinosaur Park! My favourite place!" Daisy cried.

Her friends all stared at her in confusion. "Since when?" Renee asked.

"You know what, guys?" Barbie said. "It's Daisy's big day today, so if she wants to see dinosaurs, then we'll see dinosaurs!"

Teresa, Nikki, and Renee decided to chill in the camper swimming pool while Barbie and Daisy toured Dinosaur Park.

"I really had no idea you were so into dinosaurs," Renee commented.

"Which one did you get?"

"It's a... stuffasaurus!" Daisy said, trying to hide the fact that she didn't know the dinosaur's official name. "Oh, ha. Wait. Just kidding!" She peeked at the tag. "She's a stegosaurus, of course!"

Barbie stared at Daisy. Something was weird about the way Daisy was acting. But just as she was about to ask her friend what was going on, Renee reminded them all that they still had a long trip ahead of them.

"We need to get going," Barbie told them, "if we want to get to the festival in time for Daisy's performance!"

Back in the camper, the four girls chatted excitedly about Daisy's show, but Daisy wished they would talk about something else.

"Hey! We're only two miles from Genuine Gem Cave!" she exclaimed.

"What is Genuine Gem Cave?" Teresa asked.

"Well, it's... a cave... with gems. I think..." Daisy explained. "Anyway, we should totally go now!"

"But... don't we have to be at the festival soon?" Teresa asked. Barbie could see how much the caves meant to Daisy. "Nikki, weren't you just saying that Daisy's jacket needed some cute sparkly green gems?"

"Oooh! That'd be cool!" Nikki called out from the back.

"Then let's go to Gem Cave!" Barbie said, smiling at Daisy.

At the entrance to the creepy-looking cave, they saw a sign about a ghost that legend said haunted the cave. The girls hesitated.

"C'mon, let's go!" Daisy said, waving her hand.

Everyone followed Daisy into the cave.

They were deep into one of the cave's long, dark tunnels when they heard a strange noise. Teresa remarked that it sounded an awful lot like... BATS!

Suddenly there were bats everywhere! The girls waved their arms trying to shoo away the flying creatures! When that didn't work, they ran!

They ran until they found themselves in a large clearing, filled with the most beautiful gems they had ever seen!

"Amazing!" Barbie exclaimed.

"I told you!" Daisy said. "Isn't it awesome?"

The girls agreed. The cave was magical! They wanted to explore the gems up close.

"We need to go, if we're to get to the festival in time" Barbie said, looking at the time.

Daisy made a face. "When has a concert ever started on time?" she asked.

Barbie was surprised by Daisy's reaction. She knew Daisy had dreamed of an opportunity. Why was she suddenly pretending like it was no big deal?

Daisy finally agreed that it was time to leave. "Follow me!" she said.

They walked until they stumbled upon a clearing with three tunnel entrances. Daisy headed for one of them. "Is that the way out?" Barbie asked.

"Uh, sure!" Daisy replied. The others didn't hear her add "I think" under her breath.

Later, when they ended up in exactly the same spot from where they had started, it was clear that Daisy had led them in one big circle. Daisy was so embarrassed! She felt like hiding.

"I, uh, left my mobile in that last tunnel!" she said nervously, as she ran off.

Barbie stared after her friend and thought about all the times Daisy had acted weird that day.

I'll be right back," Barbie said, going after her.

Barbie found Daisy sitting on the ground.

"Are you ok? You seem to want to do everything in the world today except the one thing you say you want to do most in the world!" Barbie said.

Daisy sighed. "I'm so nervous about DJ'ing," Daisy finally admitted. "It's sooooo many people!"

Barbie smiled. "Hey, what is it you always say?"

Daisy let out a laugh. "If you love what you do, it's worth doing no matter what!" she stated.

"Exactly," Barbie said.

A loud crash startled them.

"Barbie! Daisy! Help!" Their friends' voices were coming from another part of the cave.

They raced in the direction of the voices. Barbie shined a light into a crater and found Nikki, Teresa and Renee waving up at her.

Barbie MALIBU

"How'd you get down there?" Barbie asked.

"We were taking a selfie in that cart over there," Renee explained. "But then it started moving, and it dumped us in here! We can't get out!"

Daisy hopped up onto the broken tracks that used to run across the crater. "I got you into this mess, I'll get you out of it!" she called down to her friends.

Suddenly, Barbie appeared by her side. "We've got this!" she said confidently. "Together. On the count of three! One, two, THREE!"

On three, Barbie and Daisy jumped and landed safely on the other side! Then they found a ladder and lowered it into the crater so their friends could climb out.

After a big group hug, the girls found their way back through the tunnels and out of the cave.

They hopped back into the camper and headed to the festival – this time with no more detours!

Barbie will never forget the courage Daisy showed that day.

After all, Daisy herself said, "If I could stand on a narrow rail in a dark cave and jump over a crater, then DJ'ing for a happy crowd is not going to be a problem!"

Back at home, Barbie told her sisters all about the road trip. "Dancing in the front row was the best part!" she said.

THE END

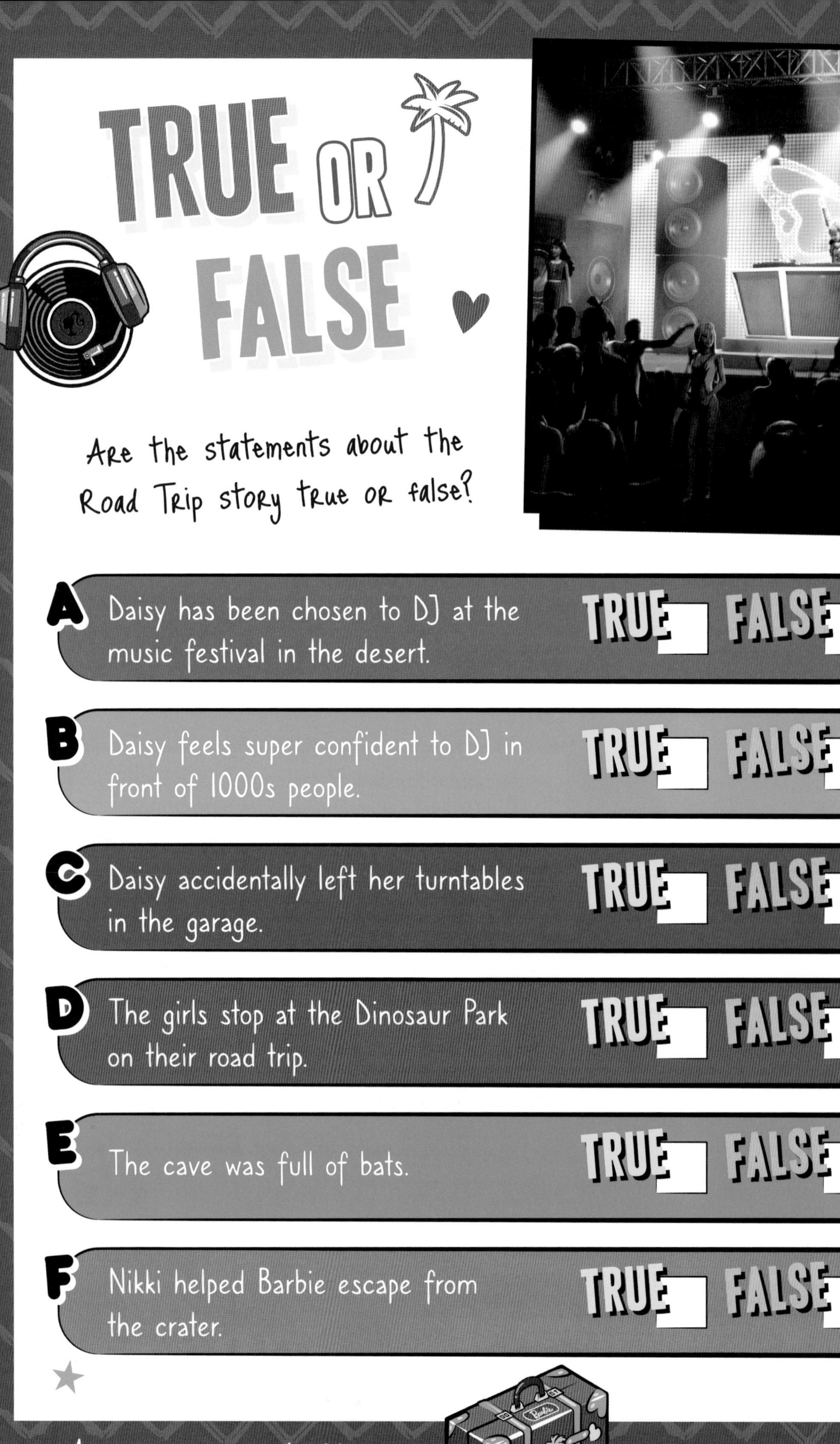

TRUE OR FALSE

Are the statements about the Road Trip story true or false?

A Daisy has been chosen to DJ at the music festival in the desert. TRUE ☐ FALSE ☐

B Daisy feels super confident to DJ in front of 1000s people. TRUE ☐ FALSE ☐

C Daisy accidentally left her turntables in the garage. TRUE ☐ FALSE ☐

D The girls stop at the Dinosaur Park on their road trip. TRUE ☐ FALSE ☐

E The cave was full of bats. TRUE ☐ FALSE ☐

F Nikki helped Barbie escape from the crater. TRUE ☐ FALSE ☐

Answers on pages 76-77

TAKE A TRIP

Do you ever think about going on a road trip with your friends? Choose what you would pack by adding the items to the suitcase.

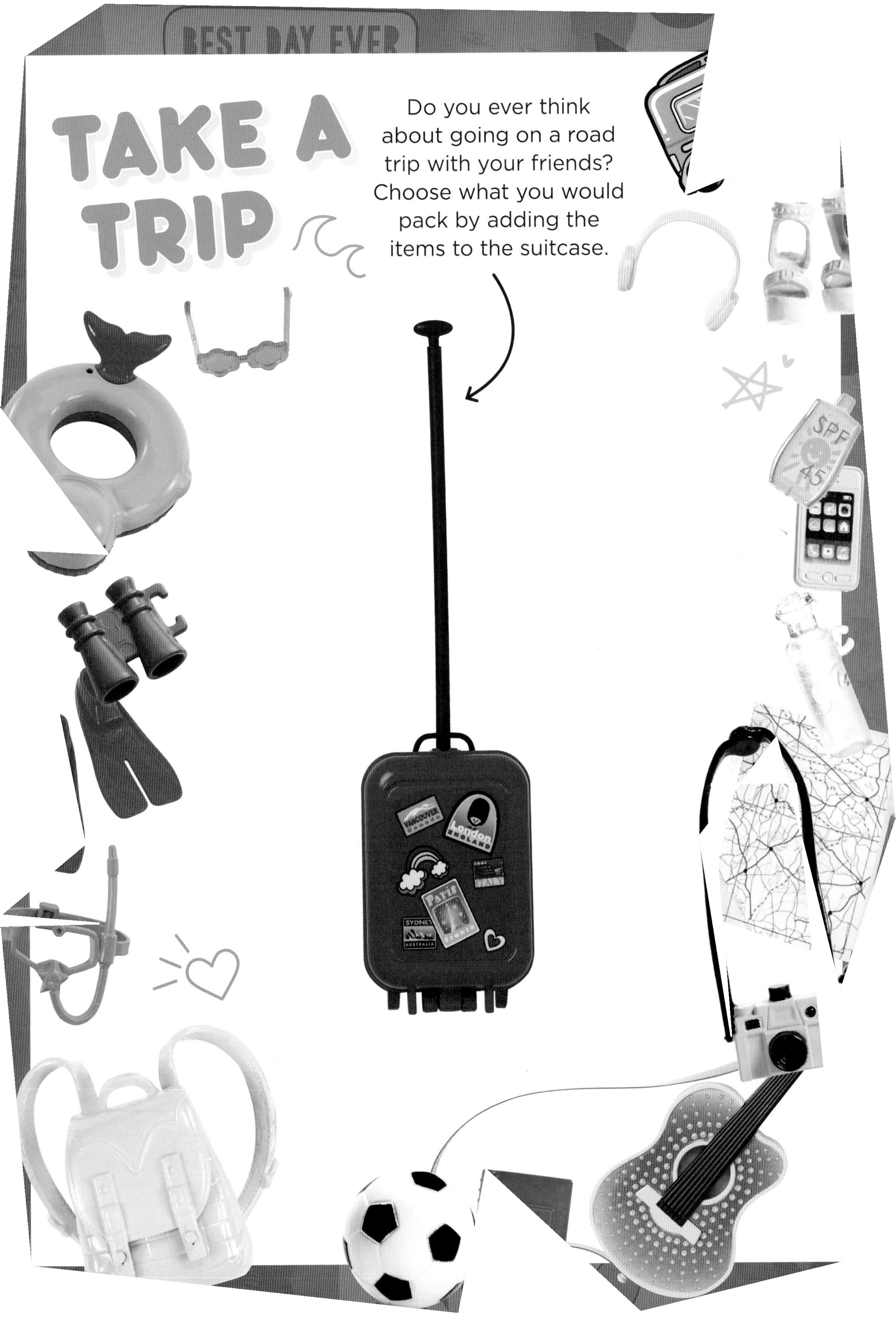

BEST *Pal* PROFILES

Teresa

This is my super smart friend, Teresa. She is such a brain box and is always excited to learn new things. I totally rely on her when I need some balanced and coolheaded advice. But don't think that she isn't completely passionate – even about weird stuff, like mould! And when she gets excited, I get to hear her talk in Spanish, which I love.

TERESA LOVES PUZZLES! HELP HER SOLVE THESE SPARKLY NUMBER PROBLEMS.

A ◆ + ◆ − ♥ =

B ⬡ − ▣ + ♥ =

C ▣ + ♥ + ◆ + ◆ =

♥ = 1
◆ = 2
▣ = 3
⬡ = 4

NIKKI

Meet Nikki, who is one-of-a-kind and a friend with a huge personality. She's so creative and is one of the most talented artists and designers I've ever met. If I ever need new fashion ideas, she's the one I go to since she's crazy into fabric crafts. I mean, she's studded some trainers, painted jeans and even added tassels to a t-shirt. Nikki is a natural entrepreneur – not only has she started her mobile snack business, she's also run for city council and manages her own dog-walking company. She's completely inspirational!

BE CREATIVE LIKE NIKKI AND CREATE A COOL DESIGN FOR THIS TRAINER

WELCOME TO WELLNESS

Why not throw a wellness party for you and your best buddies? Here are some ideas to help you and your friends relax and unwind.

SPACE TO RELAX

Create a zen-like space for your party by being outside in nature. If that's not possible, you can build a relaxing environment inside by:

- Tidying everything away that you don't need
- Lowering the lights
- Using battery-powered tealights.

DESTRESS WITH YOGA

Try these yoga poses with your friends to bring on the calm.

Stand like a tree

Stretch like a snake

Pose like a dancer

Sit and breath

Did You Know?

Colouring can help relax the brain and help ease anxiety.

TIME TO HYDRATE

Make a hydration station with jugs of water with different flavoured items in. You could try:

- Lemon and lime
- Cucumber and rosemary
- Strawberries and mint.

Did You Know?

Spending time outside in nature has been shown to reduce stress and improve health.

MIND MATTERS

Take some time to be kind to your brain by being mindful. You can practise being mindful by sitting comfortably in a quiet place and:

- Scanning through your body, making sure you think about each part.
- Breathing in deeply while counting to 3 and then out slowly while counting to 5.
- Acknowledging how you feel right now and saying it's ok to feel that way.

BEACH CLEAN-UP

After an awesome day at the beach, Barbie and her friends are getting ready to head home. Help them clear the beach by circling all the objects that shouldn't be left at the beach.

BEST DAY EVER

Answers on pages 76-77

Super Styles

Here's a little inspiration for some hair styles to try. Tick your favourites and then add your very own design to the hair band.

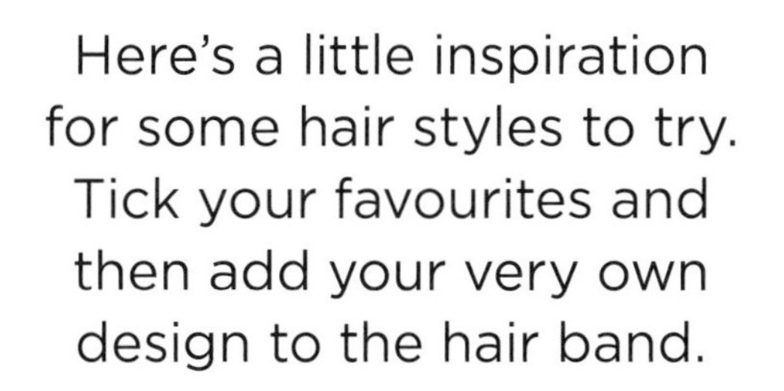

FESTIVE FUN

Barbie MALIBU

Time to test your memory!

Take a look at the seasonal scene below for 45 seconds, then cover it up and answer the questions on the opposite page.

1 What colou
aroun

2 How many blankets are on the sofa?

3 What colour are they?

4 Which friends have come to visit?

5 Are there presents under the tree?

6 What colour are Chelsea's tights?

7 Are there candy canes hanging on the tree?

8 How many stockings are hanging on the fireplace?

9 What colour is the rug under the dining table?

10 What is the gla
on the coffee table?

Renee

There's no one who tells it like it is more than my super cool friend, Renee. I love how she gets so excited about stuff and she is absolutely fearless. I mean, when she commits to an idea, she absolutely goes for it. Renee is completely courageous, outgoing and doesn't forget how to have fun. She loves athletics, skateboarding, skiing and most winter sports; she even dreams of owning her own luge one day.

Daisy

My sweet Daisy is the kindest, loveliest friend – she just simply loves people. I haven't met anyone as warm and compassionate as she is. There's no friend like her. She is also the coolest DJ that I know and is super turntable-talented. Not only does she love listening to music, but she loves loves loves to dance to it too. I think my fave thing about Daisy is her laugh – it's so big and hearty.

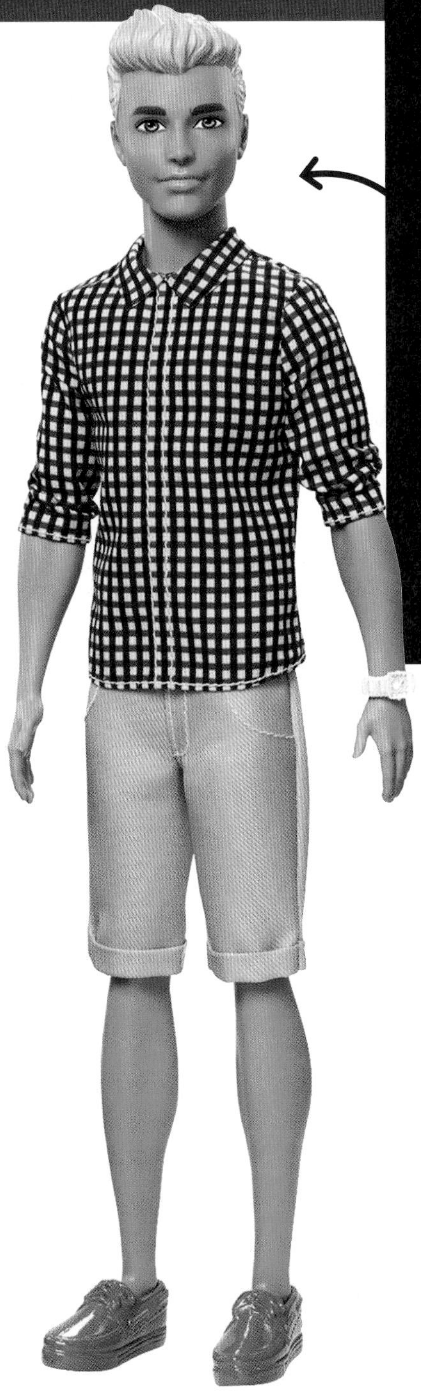

Ken

Ken is my BFF, oldest friend and next-door neighbour; he's basically like a member of my family. I'm pretty sure that he thinks my family and I are all crazy, but he still loves hanging out. There's no end to the fun we have. We bake together and there's no one I would love to have a dance battle with more. We just make each other laugh non-stop. It's no secret that Ken's favourite thing in the world is the beach and everything about it. He surfs, dives and knows a bunch about the ocean. His number one dream is to be a lifeguard.

Check out this super cute drawing of me and my friends. Why don't you colour it in with your favourite colouring pencils.

SHY

Sweet

Positive

Loud

Smart

Strong

QUIET

Serious

FUNNY

Fierce

Kind

Silly

DREAM TEAM

It takes teamwork to get through something tricky. Help Barbie's friends solve the puzzle below by finding a way through the grid. Follow the order of the objects in the key to get from start to finish.

TIP
You can move up, down, left and right.

START

FINISH

Answers on pages 76-77

BFF Squad

Barbie and her friends know how to have fun. Colour in these pictures with your favourite colouring pencils.

ADVENTURE AWAITS!

Plan your holidays with this super handy planner.

MUSIC I'D LIKE TO LISTEN TO

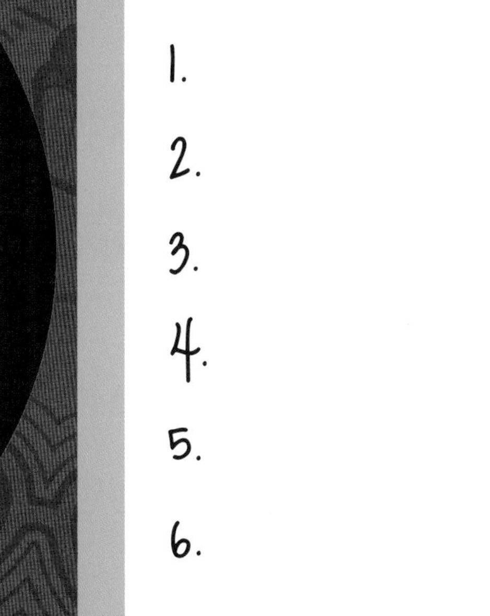

NEW THINGS I'D LIKE TO LEARN...

1.
2.
3.
4.
5.
6.

ACTIVITIES I'D LIKE TO TRY...

1.
2.
3.
4.
5.
6.
7.
8.

Books I'd like to read

Page 5

The word 'DREAMS' can be found 3 times.

1. Page 4 Contents
2. Page 46 title
3. Page 43 answer

Page 6

Page 8

S	U	R	F	I	N	G	S	X	W	H	K
S	H	O	U	I	O	S	C	H	O	O	L
Z	M	H	C	O	D	G	B	O	G	T	I
D	E	D	O	S	B	S	A	Q	F	X	B
B	D	H	N	F	Z	A	W	Q	R	Q	H
M	I	M	C	L	H	R	V	S	I	N	G
A	T	T	E	Y	U	E	O	P	E	N	C
K	A	V	R	N	A	L	A	S	N	C	B
E	T	U	T	I	O	A	A	E	D	I	O
U	E	F	D	S	A	X	A	M	S	H	U
P	A	S	I	S	T	E	R	N	A	D	V
S	D	F	H	O	M	E	W	O	R	K	B

Page 10

Page 12

DREAMER
EXPLORER
FEARLESS

Page 15

Picture c.

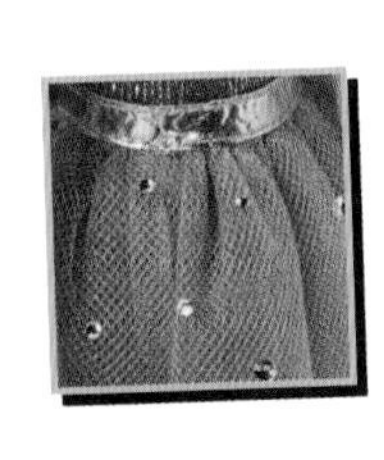

Page 17

Page 19

CHELSEA
SKIPPER
STACIE

Pages 22-23

Page 34

E is the odd picture out.

Page 35

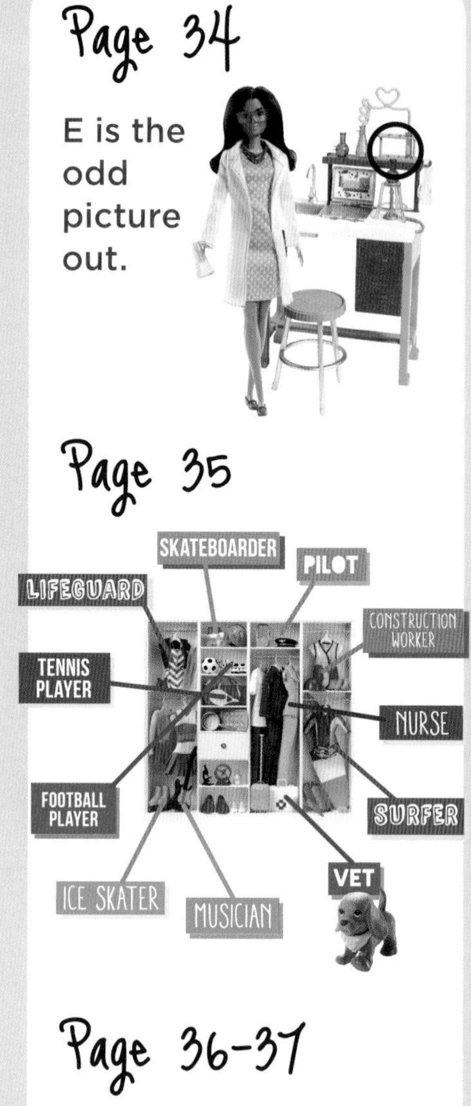

Page 36-37

A - 8, B - 2, C - 7, D - 4, E - 3, F - 1, G - 5, H - 6.

Page 38

There are 6 pets.

Page 41

Pages 42-43

LET YOUR DREAMS TAKE FLIGHT

Page 44

Page 45

E, C, D, A, F, B

Page 45

A) Palm Tree
B) Record
C) Camper

Page 46

E, D, C, B, A.

Page 47

Page 45

A) TRUE
B) FALSE
C) FALSE
D) TRUE
E) TRUE
F) FALSE

Page 48

Page 60

A) 3
B) 2
C) 8

Page 64

Page 66-67

1. pink and orange
2. three
3. red and green
4. Daisy and Teresa
5. yes
6. blue
7. no
8. three
9. pink
10. snow globe

Page 71

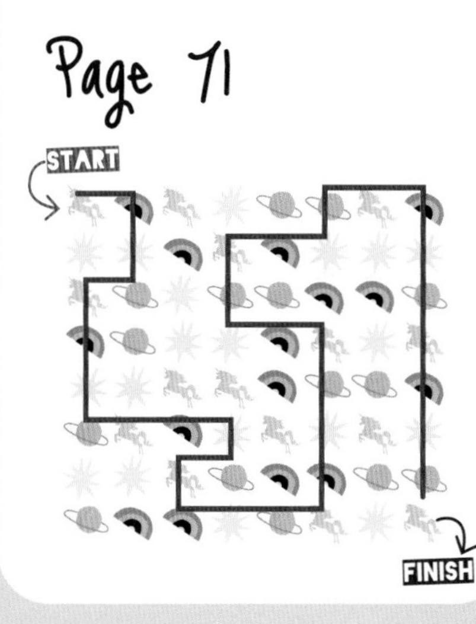